There are lots of Early Reader
stories you might enjoy.

Look at the back of the book or,
for a complete list, visit
www.orionchildrensbooks.co.uk

MERCY
and the
HIPPO

MERCY
and the
HIPPO

Lauren St John
Illustrated by Nila Aye

Orion
Children's Books

ORION CHILDREN'S BOOKS

First published in Great Britain in 2017
by Hodder and Stoughton

1 3 5 7 9 10 8 6 4 2

Text © Lauren St John 2017
Illustrations © Nila Aye 2017

A CIP catalogue record for this book
is available from the British Library.

ISBN 978 1 4440 0808 1

Printed and bound in China

The paper and board used in this book are from well-managed forests
and other responsible sources.

MIX
Paper from
responsible sources
FSC® C104740

FSC
www.fsc.org

Orion Children's Books
An imprint of
Hachette Children's Group
Part of Hodder and Stoughton
Carmelite House
50 Victoria Embankment
London EC4Y 0DZ

An Hachette UK Company
www.hachette.co.uk

www.orionchildrensbooks.co.uk

This book is dedicated to my children,
Liliana and Tom, my two very own
Mercy and Zane – Nila Aye

Contents

Chapter 1

Every day Mercy spent an hour walking to and from the well to fetch water.

There was a pond beside her
African village, but a hippo
lived there.

Mercy didn't think it was fair to wash clothes and dishes in the animal's home.

The other villagers laughed at her.

'Do you really think that fat, dumb hippo knows you're breaking your back for her?' asked Mrs Nyoni.

'It doesn't matter whether she knows or not,' said Mercy, stirring sadza in a cooking pot.

'Every living creature should be
respected. If we're kind to nature,
nature will be kind to us.'

Mercy and her little brother, Zane, were alone in the world.

The day after their mum died, the
hippo had appeared in the pond.
They named her Clara.

Every evening they sat beside
Clara's pond and watched the sun
go down in a fiery ball. For those
few minutes, they forgot about their
troubles.

Chapter 2

That summer the African sun sizzled hotter than ever. Rain was a stranger who never visited. Crops died in the field.

The pond began to shrink. Soon it hardly reached Clara's knees.

Mercy and little Zane made three trips a day to the well. They carried one bucket for themselves and two for the hippo.

It was tiring work. The sun burned down and the buckets' wire handles gave them blisters.

Mercy begged the other villagers
not to take what was left of the
hippo's pond, but they told her she
was crazy.

One morning Mrs Nyoni came to tell them that Clara was nearly dead. 'You will be glad to hear that you will no longer have to fetch water for that ungrateful river pig.'

Mercy and Zane were not
glad at all. They rushed down
to the pond.

Clara was lying on her side, gasping for breath. Her skin was cracked and dry. The villagers had taken the last of her water that morning.

'Don't give up, Clara,' pleaded
Mercy. 'We're going to do our best
to save you.'

That day, they walked to the well
five times to fetch water to pour
over the hippo.

By sundown they were trembling with exhaustion. Clara had not stirred for hours.

'Will she stay alive – not like
Mama?' asked Zane.

'I hope so but I can't promise,'
Mercy told her brother sadly.

Chapter 3

That night, a huge storm swept in.
Not even the oldest villagers had
seen a storm so fierce. Lightning
snaked across the black sky.
Thunder crashed as if giants were
playing football with boulders in
the heavens.

When the rain stopped, the
villagers came out of their huts to
find that the pond had become a
lake and joined up with a river.

There was no sign of Clara.
Mrs Nyoni said that she'd been
washed away in the flood.

With Clara gone, the children didn't have to walk to the well for water, but the sunset wasn't the same without her. They missed her terribly.

A week later, Mercy was scooping
water from the river when a
crocodile swam by.

Before she could move, the monster grabbed Mercy's dress. Zane yelled and threw stones but it was no use. It dragged her under with its massive jaws.

Suddenly, there was a tremendous splash. The crocodile let go and Mercy was free. The hippo had saved her life.

The children tried to tell the
villagers about the hippo's bravery.

'You told us that she didn't care,' Mercy said to Mrs Nyoni. 'This shows she did. It was her way of thanking us. I helped her and she helped me.'

None of the villagers believed them
– not even when Mercy showed
them the tooth marks on her leg.

Chapter 4

For weeks after the rains, Clara had
all the water she could wish for.

Then disaster struck. A factory opened upriver. It pumped out chemicals and polluted the river. Even the laziest villagers had to walk to the distant well.

Mercy and Zane knew that unless they moved on, they'd starve. Early one morning, they went to see Clara. They told her that they were going in search of a better life.

The hippo turned her back on them. She was hurt that they were leaving her. They begged her to join them, but she ignored them.

The children were very upset. The world seemed a gloomy place as they set out on their journey.

An hour later, Zane glanced over his shoulder and whooped with joy. The hippo was following them.

The three friends marched for days through the African bush. The sun beat down on them. At night, they huddled together for warmth.

Their food ran out and they struggled to find water. The children's clothes turned to rags.

On the third afternoon they saw a beautiful lake dotted with pink flamingos. A locked gate blocked their way.

Clara and Zane were too thirsty and hungry to walk another step. Mercy wanted to get help but her legs were like jelly. She leaned against Clara and slept.

Chapter 5

'I know I'm not dreaming because if I was the hippo would be in my lake with the flamingos,' said a voice.

Mercy opened her eyes.
A young man was standing
over her. 'I'm Tam,' he said.
'Are you thirsty?'

He took two bottles of orange soda
from an icebox in his Land Rover
and gave them to Mercy and Zane.

Then they poured ten bottles of
water over Clara.

Mercy thanked him a hundred
times. 'Did you say the lake was
yours?'

He nodded. 'I want to start a
wildlife sanctuary here. Trouble is,
I don't have anyone to help apart
from the caretaker.'

'What sort of people are you
hoping to hire?' Mercy asked.

Tam grinned. 'The kind of people crazy enough to take a journey across Africa with a hippo.'

'Be warned, it'll be hard work.
We'll have to help lame ostriches,
pythons tied in knots and leopards
with thorns in their paws.'

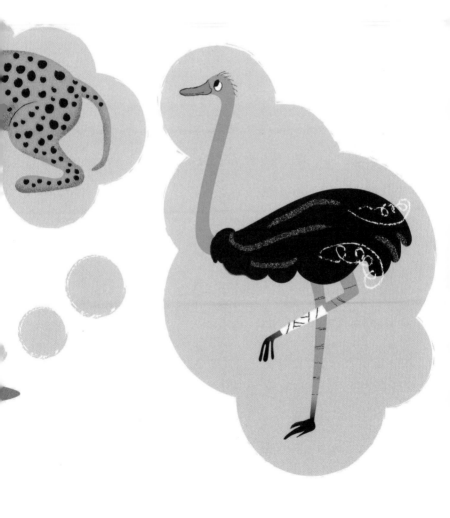

'Sounds perfect,' said Mercy.

Tam lifted Zane to his feet.
'Then you're hired. If you've
recovered enough to walk to
the lake, maybe we can show
Clara her new home ...'